G000256596

# The one that got away

### by Jan Mark

**Illustrated by**
Jan Lewis

**Series Editors**
Steve Barlow and Steve Skidmore

# The One That Got Away

Mrs Cooper's class is getting ready for a Show and Tell morning. Most of the people in Class 2 enjoy this, but Malcolm hates it. He is not shy, but he does not like standing up to talk about things in front of other people. He is afraid that they will laugh at him. Last time Class 2 had Show and Tell, he brought along his special stone, but no one could understand why it was special because he did not know what to say about it.

This time he decides that he must bring something really interesting, but he has left it too late to find anything. Then he gets hold of an empty matchbox. If only he could think of something to put in the matchbox ...

William

Mary

David

Kevin

Isobel →

Mrs Cooper
↓

James
↙

Sarah →

Malcolm

↗
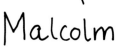

Mum
↙

# Scene 1

Home time on
Thursday afternoon.

**Mrs Cooper:**  Have you finished clearing up?

**Everybody:**  Yes, Mrs Cooper.

**Mrs Cooper:**  All right, everyone. Sit down.

*(They all sit down.)*

**Sarah:** But it's home time.

**Mrs Cooper:** I know it's home time, but I want to remind you about tomorrow.

**William and David:** What about tomorrow?

**Mrs Cooper:** You see? You've forgotten. That's why I want to remind you. Now, someone sensible, please. What have we got to remember to bring tomorrow?

**Everybody:** Something interesting, Mrs Cooper.

| | |
|---|---|
| **Mrs Cooper:** | And what are we going to do after that? |
| **Everybody:** | Stand up and talk about it, Mrs Cooper. |
| **Mrs Cooper:** | So don't forget. I hope you have all found something interesting to tell us about. |
| **Mary:** | I'm going to bring my gerbil. It's got a little cage. |
| **Mrs Cooper:** | Not now, Mary. Save it for tomorrow. All right, chairs on tables. Goodbye, Class 2. |
| **Everybody:** | Goodbye, Mrs Cooper. Goodbye, everybody. |
| **Malcolm:** | Amen. |
| **David:** | What? What did you say? |
| **Malcolm:** | I said Amen. |
| **Sarah:** | You only say Amen after prayers. |

**Malcolm:** Well, it sounds like praying when we all say things together. It comes out so slow.

**William:** He's trying to be funny. Ha. Ha. Ha. Ha.

**Mrs Cooper:** William!

**William:** Ha.

**James:** I'm bringing my fossil, tomorrow. It looks like a worm, all curled up, but my dad says it's a shell.

**Sarah:** I've got a shell. It isn't a fossil but it's ever so old. It was my granny's.

**William:** Was your granny a snail, then?

**Mary:** What are you bringing, Malcolm?

**Malcolm:** Um ...

**Isobel:** You're not bringing your stone again, are you?

**Malcolm:** Why not? You always bring your calculator.

**Isobel:** My calculator's interesting. Your old stone is boring.

**Malcolm:** No, it isn't.

**David:** Yes it is. Remember last time? Mrs Cooper said, "Why is your stone interesting?" and you didn't know.

**Malcolm:** Well ... it's a funny shape. And it's a nice colour.

**Sarah:** Yes, but it isn't interesting.

**James:** Not like my fossil. My fossil is a stone, but it's interesting. It isn't just a boring old stone.

**William:** Boring! Boring!

**Mrs Cooper:** I thought you all wanted to go home. Hurry up.

**David:** I'm bringing my conkers. What have you got, William?

**William:** My spider. It's the only spider in the world with five legs.

**David:** It can't be a spider then. Spiders have eight legs. Don't they, Miss?

**Sarah:** Insects have six legs and spiders have eight. You told us that, Miss.

**Mrs Cooper:** I want to go home, even if you don't. Get your coats on.

**Isobel and Mary:** Yes, Miss. Goodnight, Miss.

**David:** That thing you've got. It can't be a spider if it's only got five legs.

**William:** It is a spider. It had an accident.

**Mary:** Yuk! I hate creepy-crawlies.

**Mrs Cooper:** There aren't any creepy-crawlies here – except you lot.
Now, GO HOME!

# Scene 2

Teatime on Thursday evening,
at Malcolm's house.

**Mum:** Malcolm, what are you doing with that stone?

**Malcolm:** It's my special stone.

**Kevin:** It's his pet stone. He talks to it. It lives in the garden and every time he goes past, he says hello to it.

**Mum:** Take it out of the sink, Malcolm. I want to wash up.

**Malcolm:** I'm giving it a bath.

**Kevin:** You aren't going to take it to school again, are you?

**Mum:** Why do you want to take it to school?

**Malcolm:** I don't, but it's Show and Tell again. I don't know what else to take. Last time I took my stone, everyone said it was boring.

**Mum:** Well, it isn't very exciting, is it?

**Kevin:** He makes it do tricks. He says, "Sit up and beg," and then he puts a lump of sugar on its nose.

**Malcolm:** You, shut up!

**Mum:** Stop fighting, you two. Malcolm, please take it out of the sink.

**Malcolm:** What can I take for Show and Tell? It's tomorrow.

**Mum:** Why do you always leave things till the last minute?

**Malcolm:** I don't. Mrs Cooper told us on Monday, but I can't think of anything else to take.

**Kevin:** What about your interesting twig that looks like a stick-insect?

**Mum:** Yes, but it isn't a stick-insect.

**Kevin:** What about your interesting marble that looks like a glass eye? What about your interesting penny with a hole in it?

**Mum:** Kevin, stop it. You aren't being very helpful.

15

**Kevin:** I know! Take the Siamese twins.

**Mum:** What Siamese twins?

**Kevin:** He's got these two jelly babies stuck together, back to back.

**Mum:** Oh, those. I wish you would throw them away, Malcolm. They are stuck to the bookshelf, as well.

**Malcolm:** I'll eat them.

*(He picks up a matchbox from the table.)*

**Malcolm:** Can I have this matchbox?

**Mum:** Yes, if it's empty.

**Kevin:** Are you going to take that for Show and Tell? "Good morning, everybody. Today Malcolm is going to tell us about his interesting matchbox."

**Mum:** Kevin!

**Malcolm:** *(Opening the matchbox upside down)* Whoops!

**Mum:** Oh, Malcolm. Now you've dropped all the matches.

**Malcolm:** This box has got the same label on both sides. You can't tell which way up it is.

**Kevin:** Trust you to open it upside down.

**Malcolm:** Well, can I have it? You can put the matches in this other box.

**Mum:** *You* can put the matches in this other box. Go on, pick them up.

**Kevin:** You could put a beetle into that matchbox.

**Malcolm:** Yes, but I haven't got a beetle.

*(He picks up the matches.)*

**Malcolm:** Can I take Alfred to school?

**Kevin:** "Ladies and gentlemen, here is Alfred, the world's most interesting cat. I brought him to school in a matchbox."

**Mum:** No, of course you can't take Alfred to school.

**Malcolm:** What about the fish?

**Mum:** No, not the fish. How could you carry the tank?

**Kevin:**   Roll up! Roll up! Come and see the interesting fish!

**Mum:**   Kevin, if you don't stop this, I shall let Malcolm take you to Show and Tell as the world's most boring brother.

**Malcolm:**   Nyaaaaaaaaaa!

19

# Scene 3

Friday morning,
in the classroom.

**Kevin:** Have you got your interesting stone, Malcolm?

**Malcolm:** No.

**Kevin:** What have you got for Show and Tell, then?

**Malcolm:** It's a secret.

**Kevin:** Is it that matchbox? What's inside it?

**Malcolm:** Nothing. It's a secret. Go away.

**Kevin:** "Ladies and gentlemen, here is the world's most interesting matchbox!"

**Mrs Cooper:** Kevin, I thought you were in Class 5.

**Kevin:** Yes, Miss.

**Mrs Cooper:** Then you'd better get along there, hadn't you? Or do you want to join Class 2 today?

**Kevin:** No thanks, Miss.

**Mrs Cooper:** Come along, Class 2. Sit down and stop talking. Have you got your interesting things ready?

**Mary:** Yes, Miss. I've got my gerbil. It's in this little cage, look.

**Mrs Cooper:** Not now, Mary. Wait until we start.

**Isobel:** Can I go first?

**Mrs Cooper:** I think Mary had better go first, before she bursts. You next, Isobel.

**Mary:** *(Holding up a little cage)* This is my gerbil. Her name is Sally. At home we keep her in a tank.

**William:** Is it full of water?

**James:** Does she swim?

**David:** She's a water-gerbil!

**Mary:** No, the tank's got earth in it. Gerbils live in burrows. I'm going to take her home at dinner time so she can go back down her hole. She used to have a husband called Joe but she had too many babies, so now she just lives with another lady gerbil. That's all.

**Mrs Cooper:** Thank you, Mary. I should put a cloth over Sally's cage, if I were you. Right, now your turn, Isobel.

**Isobel:** *(Showing her calculator)* I got this calculator for my birthday. Now I'm going to press these numbers. 7. 3. 8. 0. 5. 1. Now I'm going to turn it upside down and it says ISOBEL.

**Sarah:** You did that last time.

**Isobel:** No one else can do it. You can't write SARAH on a calculator.

**Mrs Cooper:** Thank you very much, Isobel. Now, how about you, Malcolm? Come up here to the front. What have you got to show us?

**Malcolm:** *(Holding out the matchbox)* Here it is, Miss.

**Mrs Cooper:** A matchbox?

**Malcolm:** *(Opening the matchbox)* It's in the matchbox – oh!

*(He crawls about on the floor.)*

**Mrs Cooper:** Malcolm, what's the matter? What are you doing under the desk?

**Malcolm:** It's fallen out!

**Mrs Cooper:** What's fallen out?

**Malcolm:** It's a ... a ... it's got six legs and sharp knees and frilly ginger eyebrows on stalks.

**Mary:** Oh! A creepy-crawly!

**Malcolm:** There it goes!

*(He leaps after it.)*

**Mrs Cooper:** Where?

**Malcolm:** Missed it. Hey, it's running under your chair, Mary!

**Mary:** *(Climbing on the table)* Eeeeeeeeeeeeh!

**Mrs Cooper:** Mary, get off that table. Get down.

**William:** I see it!

**David:** *(Flinging a book)* There it goes!

**Mrs Cooper:** David, don't throw books about.

**James:** *(Stamping on the floor)* I got it! I killed it!

**Mary:** Help, Miss. Ow, help! I felt it on my leg.

**Sarah:** It's crawling up the curtain.

**Isobel:** It's on the ceiling.

**William:** Wooo! It's fallen in your hair, Mary.

**Mary:** *(Panicking)* Ah — ah — aaaaaaaaaaaaah!

**Mrs Cooper:** Mary, be quiet. Stop screaming. There's nothing in your hair. Sit down, everybody. Now, Malcolm, where's your creature?

**Malcolm:** I think it flew out of the window, Miss.

**Mrs Cooper:** I hope it did. Next time we have Show and Tell, Malcolm, you had better bring something that does not move about.

**Malcolm:** Yes, Miss. I'll bring my stone.

The End

# Teachers' Notes

## The One That Got Away

### Choosing Parts

The characters of Mrs Cooper, Malcolm, Kevin, Mum, Mary and Isobel will need confident readers. William, David, James and Sarah have shorter parts.

### Classroom Organisation

*The One That Got Away* is written so that a whole class could take part in a reading. However, you may prefer to let a smaller group of children read and act out the scripts. There are ten named parts, but it would be easy for confident readers to double up roles. You could read the script through with the whole class before allowing smaller groups to act out the play. Alternatively, you could ask groups of different sizes to work on different scenes, before bringing the groups back as a whole class to put the play together.

### Putting On the Play

You may wish to put on a performance of the play, rather than just reading it. The following suggestions may provide you with a starting point for your own ideas about staging a production. Obviously, the use you make of these suggestions will vary depending on the time and resources available to your school.

For permission to put on a profit making performance of *The One That Got Away*, please contact the Editorial Department, Ginn and Co Ltd, Prebendal House, Parson's Fee, Aylesbury, Bucks HP20 2QY.

(There is no need to apply for permission if you are not charging an entrance fee, but please let us know if you are putting on any performance of this play, as we would be interested to hear about it.)

### Staging

The play has three scenes. Scenes 1 and 3 are set in a classroom. Scene 2 is set in the kitchen of Malcolm's house. The classroom can easily be set up with tables and chairs which can then be moved to represent the kitchen. In order to differentiate between the scenes, lighting changes could be used. An alternative idea is to have the two settings as separate areas. This arrangement would give opportunity for a more elaborate set, with kitchen units and appropriate props.

### Costumes

The children can wear their school clothes. They will also need coats, scarves and bags for Scene 1. Mum and Mrs Cooper should dress as adults.

### Props

- School bags and books for the children in the classroom scenes.
- **Malcolm's** stone.
- Pots and pans to go in the kitchen.
- A matchbox with matches in, on the kitchen table.
- A gerbil in a cage (or an empty cage) for **Mary**.
- A calculator for **Isobel**.

# Follow-up Work

### Show and Tell

Organise a Show and Tell session. Discuss the sort of items the children could bring in first. Perhaps make it a regular feature if time allows.

## Group Discussion

- What type of people are the various characters? Who is the noisiest? The rudest? The most interesting? The funniest?
- Which character do the children like best?
- Did Malcolm really have anything in the matchbox?

## Matchbox Competition

Organise a matchbox competition to see who can get most items in to a single matchbox. You may wish to organise this as a sponsored event.

## Artwork

Ask the children to draw or paint what they think might have been in Malcolm's matchbox.

## Drama

### Make a Monster Insect!

Instead of painting or drawing what might have been in Malcolm's matchbox, the children could create their own insect by working in pairs. They can pull faces and use both their bodies to create eight-legged insects.

### Verbal Boxing: brothers and sisters

Kevin and Malcolm argue with each other. Ask the children who have brothers and sisters if this is a realistic scene. Do the children argue with their brothers and sisters? What about?

Ask two children to be a brother and sister. They are arguing about one of the following situations:

- One wants a different television programme on.
- One wants to borrow something off the other, who won't lend it.
- One of the two has broken the other's favourite game.

Ask the children to observe the following rules:

- They must sit facing each other.
- They have one minute to have the argument.
- No bad language.
- No threatening.
- No touching.

After one minute the class can vote on who has made the best argument. That person stays on, and another pupil challenges them with a different situation.